Maths BASICS

FOR AGES
9-10
KEY STAGE 2

Contents

How to use this book

Numeracy Basics helps you to help your child practise many important basic skills covered in the *National Numeracy Strategy* and *National Curriculum*.

Each book is divided into *30 units* of work which focus on *one clear* objective.

Most of the units are designed using the same easy-to-follow *key features*. In some cases these features are combined into one activity, offering further practice where appropriate.

Title
Target learning objective.

Look and learn
Introduces and explains the target objective. Provides an example to illustrate it.

Practice
Provides straightforward practice activities based on the target objective.

Challenge
Provides activities to extend and challenge.

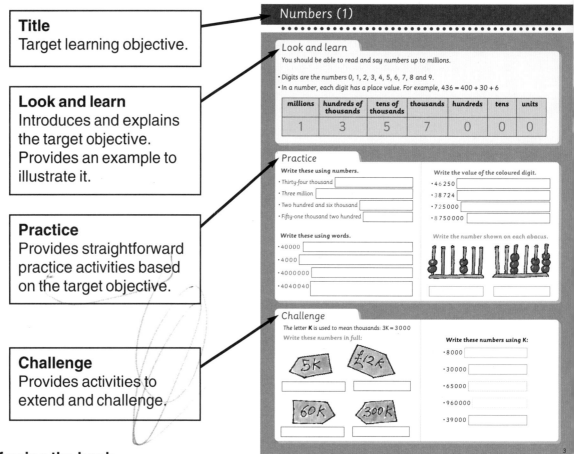

Numbers (1)

Look and learn
You should be able to read and say numbers up to millions.

- Digits are the numbers 0, 1, 2, 3, 4, 5, 6, 7, 8 and 9.
- In a number, each digit has a place value. For example, 436 = 400 + 30 + 6

millions	hundreds of thousands	tens of thousands	thousands	hundreds	tens	units
1	3	5	7	0	0	0

Practice
Write these using numbers.
- Thirty-four thousand
- Three million
- Two hundred and six thousand
- Fifty-one thousand two hundred

Write the value of the coloured digit.
- 46 250
- 38 724
- 725 000
- 8 750 000

Write these using words.
- 40 000
- 4 000
- 4 000 000
- 4 040 040

Write the number shown on each abacus.

Challenge
The letter **K** is used to mean thousands: 3K = 3 000
Write these numbers in full:

5K   £12k

60K   300K

Write these numbers using K:
- 8 000
- 30 000
- 65 000
- 960 000
- 39 000

Suggested way of using the book

- It is suggested that your child works systematically through the book.

- Try tackling one unit per week.

- Read through and discuss the *Look and learn* section with your child to make sure the key objective is understood.

- Help your child get started on the Practice section.

- After this, your child can start to work fairly independently through the page, but will need further support and encouragement.

- The answers are supplied at the end of the book for checking each unit on its completion.

Enjoy the book!

Numbers (1)

Look and learn

You should be able to read and say numbers up to millions.

- Digits are the numbers 0, 1, 2, 3, 4, 5, 6, 7, 8 and 9.
- In a number, each digit has a place value. For example, 436 = 400 + 30 + 6

millions	hundreds of thousands	tens of thousands	thousands	hundreds	tens	units
1	3	5	7	0	0	0

Practice

Write these using numbers.

- Thirty-four thousand
- Three million
- Two hundred and six thousand
- Fifty-one thousand two hundred

Write these using words.

40000

4000

4000000

4040040

Write the value of the coloured digit.

- 46 250
- 38 724
- 725 000
- 8 750 000

Write the number shown on each abacus.

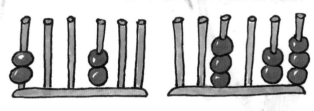

Challenge

The letter **K** is used to mean thousands: 3K = 3000

Write these numbers in full:

Write these numbers using K:

8000

30000

65000

960000

39000

Look and learn

- Multiples are the answers to multiplication tables.

- The multiples of 5 are 5, 10, 15, 20 . . .

- The multiples of 9 are 9, 18, 27, 36 . . .

- The multiples of 12 are 12, 24, 36, 48 . . .

- Factors divide exactly into the number.

- The factors of 10 are 1, 2, 5 and 10.

- The factors of 9 are 1, 3 and 9.

- The factors of 12 are 1, 2, 3, 4, 6 and 12.

Practice

Answer these as quickly as you can.

- $7 \times 8 =$
- $4 \times 8 =$
- $9 \times 7 =$
- $8 \times 6 =$
- $7 \times 7 =$
- $8 \times 9 =$
- $7 \times 6 =$
- $6 \times 9 =$
- $9 \times 3 =$
- $9 \times 9 =$

- $64 \div 8 =$
- $45 \div 9 =$
- $56 \div 7 =$
- $72 \div 8 =$
- $42 \div 6 =$
- $81 \div 9 =$
- $54 \div 6 =$
- $63 \div 9 =$
- $48 \div 6 =$
- $36 \div 4 =$

- Which number of less than 50 is a multiple of both 6 and 7?

- Which three multiples of 3, less than 20, are not a multiple of 6.

- Which multiple of 6 lies between 60 and 70?

- Complete the table.

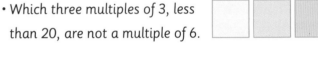

In	7		6		
Out		28		56	63

Challenge

Complete this arrow diagram. The → arrow means 'is a factor of'.

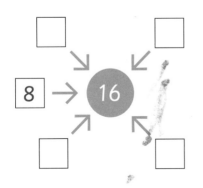
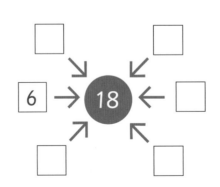
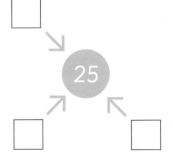

Problems

Look and learn

It is useful to remember comparative measures.

| 1 kilogram = 1000 grams |
| 1kg = 1000g |

| 1.25kg = 1250g |
| 3.5kg = 3500g |

| 1 litre = 1000 millilitres |
| 1l = 1000ml |

| 2.75l = 2750ml |
| 0.5l = 500ml |

Practice

Use these weights to help answer the questions.

• How many 200g weights are in 1 kilogram?

• How many 500g weights are in 1 kilogram?

• How many 20g weights are in $\frac{1}{2}$ kilogram?

• Using the fewest number of the weights, make up these masses. Each weight can be used more than once.

195g   1.4kg

380g

470g

1.25kg   2.3kg

Challenge

Match the labels to the containers.

1.25l

 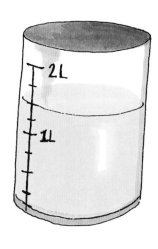 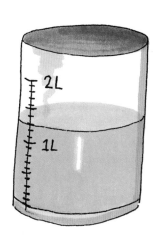

1.5l

1.3l

Look and learn

Try to remember the words used to describe fractions.

$\dfrac{4}{5}$ ← numerator
← denominator

$\dfrac{2}{5} = \dfrac{4}{10}$ ← equivalent fractions are worth the same.

↓ whole number

$1\dfrac{2}{3}$ ← fraction

A mixed number has a whole number and a fraction.

$\dfrac{4}{3}$ ← the numerator is larger than the denominator

Improper fractions have the numerator larger than the denominator.

Practice

• Write the equivalent fractions of the coloured segments.

 □ = □   □ = □

• Cross out the fraction which is not equivalent.

$\dfrac{1}{2}$ → $\dfrac{2}{4}$ $\dfrac{5}{10}$ $\dfrac{4}{8}$ $\dfrac{2}{5}$

$\dfrac{3}{4}$ → $\dfrac{12}{16}$ $\dfrac{6}{8}$ $\dfrac{15}{20}$ $\dfrac{14}{16}$

$\dfrac{2}{3}$ → $\dfrac{4}{6}$ $\dfrac{6}{9}$ $\dfrac{12}{15}$ $\dfrac{8}{12}$

• Write <, >, or = to make each statement true.

$\dfrac{2}{6}$ □ $\dfrac{1}{3}$ $\dfrac{3}{4}$ □ $\dfrac{2}{3}$ $\dfrac{1}{4}$ □ $\dfrac{4}{3}$ $\dfrac{9}{10}$ □ $\dfrac{3}{4}$ $\dfrac{11}{8}$ □ $1\dfrac{3}{8}$

Challenge

Change these improper fractions to mixed numbers.

$\dfrac{7}{5}$ → □

$\dfrac{10}{8}$ → □

$\dfrac{15}{4}$ → □

Change these mixed numbers to improper fractions.

$1\dfrac{2}{3}$ → □

$2\dfrac{3}{4}$ → □

$3\dfrac{5}{8}$ → □

What must be added to make each mixed fraction up to the next whole number?

$1\dfrac{3}{5}$ → □

$2\dfrac{7}{10}$ → □

Ratio

Look and learn

Ratios are used to compare two quantities. When referring to ratios we use words such as 'out of' and 'in every'.

7 out of 10 marbles have a red stripe.

$6 \times 7 = 42$ ✓ $8 \times 8 = 54$ ✗

$3 \times 5 = 15$ ✓ $9 \times 6 = 54$ ✓

$4 \times 7 = 28$ ✓ $10 \times 4 = 40$ ✓

$3 \times 8 = 21$ ✗ $3 \times 3 = 9$ ✓

$2 \times 10 = 20$ ✓ $8 \times 4 = 32$ ✓

8 out of 10 are correct.

Practice

2 in every 5 Queen's heads are blue, the rest are yellow. Colour the stamps. How many heads are yellow?

2 in every 4 squares are blue, the rest are red. Draw 8 squares and colour them.

Every fourth beetle is green. Draw in the missing green beetles. How many are there?

For every 2 circles, there are 3 squares. Draw the missing squares.

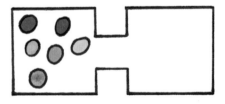

Challenge

1. A chicken must be cooked for 45 minutes for every kg. How long will it take to cook a 2kg chicken?

2. $\frac{1}{2}$ teaspoon of salt is required for each 500g of flour. How much salt is needed for $1\frac{1}{2}$ kg of flour?

3. The juice of $\frac{1}{2}$ lemon is needed for each litre of sauce. How many lemons are needed for 3 litres?

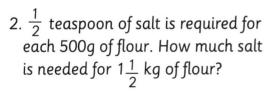

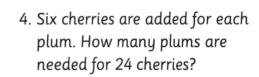

4. Six cherries are added for each plum. How many plums are needed for 24 cherries?

5. For each 25g of raisins, 50g of sultanas are needed. How many sultanas are needed for 50g of raisins?

Data (1)

Look and learn

A graph was drawn to show shoe sizes of some pupils in a class.

Graphs have axes –
a **vertical** axis and
a **horizontal** axis.
Each axis shows information.

Practice

Answer the questions using the graph above.

1. How many pupils took size 5 shoes? ☐

2. Which shoe size occurred most often? ☐

3. Which was the largest shoe size? ☐

4. How many pupils were asked about their shoe sizes altogether? ☐

5. How many pupils took more than a size 3 shoe? ☐

Challenge

This graph shows vouchers collected for school books.

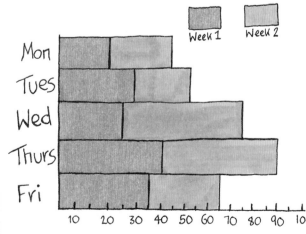

1. During week 1, when were most vouchers collected? ☐

2. During week 2, when were most vouchers collected? ☐

3. How many vouchers were collected on Thursday of week 2? ☐

4. How many vouchers were collected during week 1? ☐

5. In which week were fewest vouchers collected? ☐

Shape (1)

Look and learn

Equilateral triangle

Isosceles and right angle

Isosceles triangle

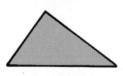

Scalene triangle

- Equilateral = 3 sides the same length.
- Isosceles = 2 sides the same length.
- Scalene = no sides the same length.

Congruent triangles are the same shape and size.

Practice

Complete the table. You can use a ruler to help.

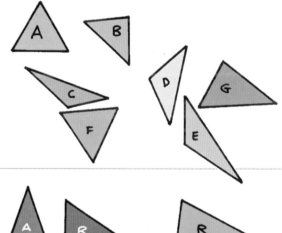

	A	B	C	D	E	F	G
Equilateral	✓						
Isosceles							
Scalene							

Complete the table.
Write which triangles are congruent to A and B.

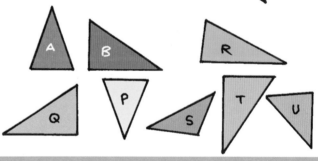

Triangle	Congruent triangles
A	P
B	

Challenge

Name each shape. Draw in all the lines of symmetry.

 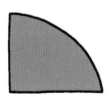 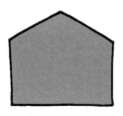 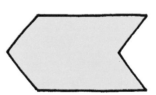 

r _ _ _ _ _ _ _   q _ _ _ _ _ _ _   p _ _ _ _ _ _   h _ _ _ _ _ _   o _ _ _ _ _ _

Check your spelling.

Measures

Look and learn

The start (or prefix) of some measuring words are helpful to learn.

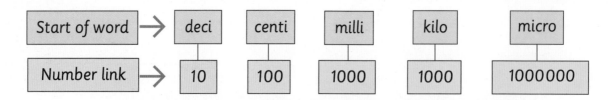

Start of word →	deci	centi	milli	kilo	micro
Number link →	10	100	1000	1000	1000000

1kg 400g = 1.4kg	2l 300ml = 2.3l	4m 50cm = 4.5m

Practice

Answer these.

[   ] cm = 1 metre

[   ] mm = 1 metre

[   ] m = 1km

[   ] dm = 1 metre

[   ] g = 1kg

[   ] ml = 1 litre

[   ] cl = 1 litre

[   ] dl = 1 litre

Look at the readings on the scales. Write each weight.
For example, 1.4 kg.

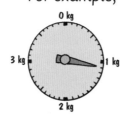

[   ]

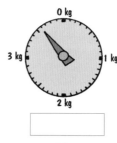

[   ]

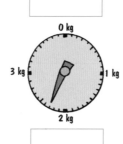

[   ]

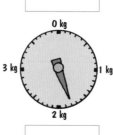

[   ]

Challenge

Answer these.

[   ] kilograms = 1 tonne

[   ] microseconds = 1 second

[   ] years = 1 millennium

[   ] centilitres = 1 decilitre

$\frac{1}{2}$ kg = [   ] g

$\frac{1}{2}$ l = [   ] ml

$\frac{1}{2}$ l = [   ] dl

$\frac{1}{2}$ l = [   ] cl

1 hour = [   ] seconds

1 week = [   ] hours

Addition and subtraction (1)

Look and learn

You can add numbers in any order:

$243 + 74 = 74 + 243$

You cannot subtract numbers in any order:

$243 - 74$ is not the same as $74 - 243$

When you subtract a larger number from a smaller number, the answer is a **negative** number.

For example, $3 - 7 = -4$

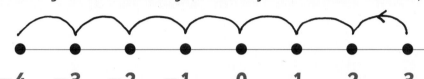

−4 −3 −2 −1 0 1 2 3 4 5 6

Practice

- Total 54, 37 and 98.
- Subtract 13 from 8.
- Find the difference between 374 and 1000.
- Increase 896 by 84.
- Decrease 706 by 48.
- Add 36 to 484.

[   ] $+ 84 = 100$

[   ] $- 56 = 16$

$47 +$ [   ] $= 120$

$127 -$ [   ] $= 78$

$37 +$ [   ] $+15 = 100$

$78 -$ [   ] $-19 = 20$

- Total £1.27, £2.35 and £3.66.
- What is the change from £10 after spending £6.48?
- Cut 2.8m from a 3.7m strip of tape. What length is left?
- Add 45ml of water to 95ml of squash. What is the total amount?

Challenge

9
473
56
2044

Choose three numbers at a time from the cloud. Find all the totals you can.

Choose two numbers from the cloud. Find all the differences you can.

Look and learn

Negative numbers come before zero on a number line.

– 3 is sometimes written like this ⁻3.

– 3 is said as 'negative three' or 'minus three'.

| −4 | −3 | −2 | −1 | 0 | 1 | 2 | 3 | 4 | 5 | 6 |

Practice

Write the missing numbers. Explain the rule for each pattern.

38	49	☐	☐	82	rule →	
1	☐	☐	16	25	rule →	
5	−1	−7	☐	☐	rule →	
63	70	☐	☐	91	rule →	
30	15	☐	☐	−30	rule →	
2	4	☐	16	☐	rule →	

Challenge

Write 'true' or 'false' for each of these statements.

• Adding two even numbers always gives an even number. ☐

• Adding three odd numbers always gives an even number. ☐

• The product of two odd numbers is always an odd number. ☐

• The difference between odd numbers is always an even number. ☐

• Two odd numbers added to an even number give an even number. ☐

Place value

Look and learn

When you round to the nearest 10, 100 or 1000, the half-way position is important.

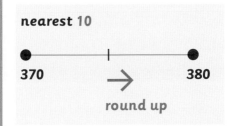

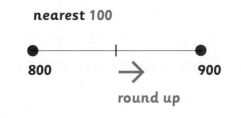

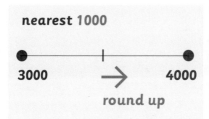

Numbers which are half-way or beyond are rounded up. The rest are rounded down.

Practice

Round these to the nearest 10:

55	73	428	604	2319

Round these to the nearest 100:

450	374	1250	6327	4664

Round these to the nearest 1000:

3500	6490	13250	15640	27399

Look at these numbers →

490	990	375	6090	9994

Make each number 10 more:

Make each number 10 times more:

Challenge

Write the correct missing numbers.

36000g =	kg	8000ml =	litres	400000mm =	m
8000g =	kg	40000ml =	litres	71000mm =	m
45000g =	kg	457000ml =	litres	5000mm =	m
20000g =	kg	850000ml =	litres	10000mm =	m

Multiplication and division (2)

Look and learn

You can check multiplication by dividing.

$$47 \times 8 = 376$$

check $8\overline{)376}$ → 47

You can check division by multiplying.

$7\overline{)98}$ → 14

check $14 \times 7 = 98$

Practice

Look at the number machines and complete the tables.

in → ×5 out →

in	17		46	
out		95		120

in → ×7 out →

in	24		76	
out		161		385

Write the missing numbers.

- 90 × [   ] = 360
- 600 × [   ] = 3600
- [   ] × 3 = 360
- [   ] × 50 = 350
- 200 × [   ] = 40000
- 80 × [   ] = 1600

Challenge

This table shows how much foreign money can be changed for £1.

Belgium	59 francs
Denmark	11 kroner
Israel	6 shekels
Japan	156 yen
Austria	21 schillings

- How many francs in £8?
- How many yen in £7?
- How many schillings in £40?
- How many shekels in £115?
- How many kroner in £125? [   ]

Practice

• A recipe needs 25g of butter, 250g of flour and 75g of sugar.
What is the total weight of these ingredients?

• Drinks cost 35p and baps cost 60p.
What is the total cost of 4 drinks and 3 baps?

• There are 264 pupils in a school hall. If 45 more enter, how many pupils will that make?

• Simon buys a coat for £54 and trousers for £39.
How much change will he get from £100?

 a. 345g
 b. 750g
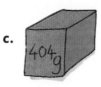 c. 404g
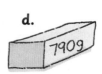 d. 790g
 e. 1320g

• What is the difference in weight between the heaviest and lightest parcels?

• How much heavier is **d** than **c**?

• What do all the parcels weigh together?

• Which two parcels have a difference of 445g?

Challenge

How much change would you get from £20 for each shopping list?

 £3.59 £1.99
 Toothpaste £1.25
 £4.99
 £2.15

1 shampoo	3 toothbrushes	3 soaps
2 soaps	1 toothpaste	1 face cream
1 face cream	1 shampoo	2 shampoos

Look and learn

The decimal point separates whole numbers from tenths.

4·3

↗ 4 whole units   ↖ 3 tenths

Two numbers after the decimal point shows hundredths.

6·45 ← 5 hundredths

↗ 6 whole units   ↑ 4 tenths

The position of zeros is important.

4·2 = 4·20 but 0·3 is not equal to 0·03

Practice

• What is the digit 3 worth in each of these numbers?

43·2 [   ]   17·3 [   ]   36.4 [   ]   0.23 [   ]

• Write the decimal number each arrow points to.

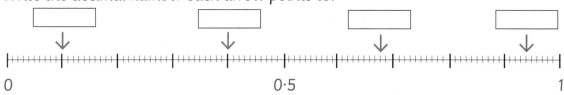

0   0·5   1

• Each triangle's total is in the middle. Write the missing corner number.

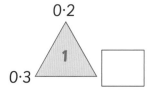 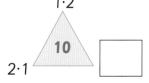 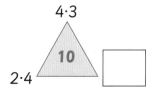 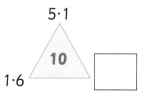

0·2
1
0·3 [   ]

1·2
10
2·1 [   ]

4·3
10
2·4 [   ]

5·1
10
1·6 [   ]

Challenge

Write these as decimals.

$2\frac{1}{2}$ → [   ]

$3\frac{1}{4}$ → [   ]

$7\frac{3}{4}$ → [   ]

Write these as fractions.

2·25 → [   ]

7·5 → [   ]

8·75 → [   ]

Write <, > or = between the numbers.

1·9 [   ] $1\frac{1}{4}$

4·5 [   ] $4\frac{1}{2}$

2·2 [   ] $2\frac{3}{4}$

Shape (2)

Look and learn

Lines of symmetry are not always horizontal or vertical.

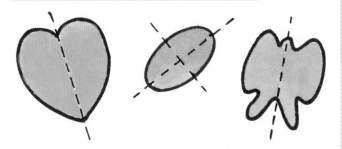

Always check that you have found **all** the lines of symmetry.

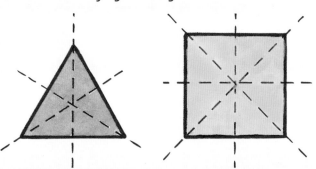

Practice

Draw **all** the lines of symmetry on each of these shapes.

Draw the other half of these shapes to make them symmetrical.

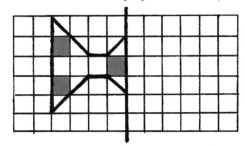 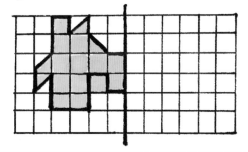

Challenge

Draw the diagonals on these quadrilaterals.
If a diagonal is also a line of symmetry, draw it in red.

 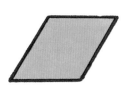   

Data (2)

Look and learn

The **mode** is the number which occurs most often.
The **range** is the difference between the highest and lowest numbers.

4 5 5 6 7 7 7 7 8 8 9

- **Mode** = 7 (it occurs most often)
- **Range** = 5 (it is 9 − 4)

Practice

Name	Shoe size
Alex	5
Beth	4
Claire	3·5
Dela	5
Emma	3
Fiona	4·5
Gareth	5
Henry	5
Ian	4
Joanne	3

- What is the mode?

- What is the range?

- Who has smaller feet than Ian?

- Who has larger feet that Fiona?

- Who takes size 3·5 shoes?

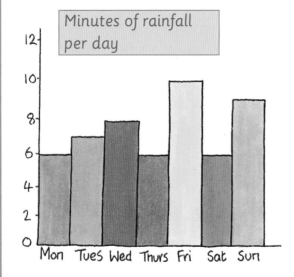

Minutes of rainfall per day

12
10
8
6
4
2
0
Mon Tues Wed Thurs Fri Sat Sun

- What is the mode?

- What is the range?

- Which was the wettest day?

- Which days were wetter than Wednesday?

- How many minutes of rain fell during the whole week?

Measures and area

Look and learn

The **area** of a rectangle = length × breadth.   The **perimeter** is the distance around the edge.

5cm

Area = 5 × 4
= 20cm²

4cm

5cm

4cm

Perimeter = 18cm
= 5 + 4 + 5 + 4
= 18cm

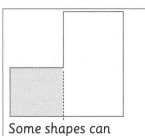

Some shapes can broken into rectangles.

Practice

Calculate the area and perimeter of each shape.

a.

12cm

3cm

perimeter =
area =

perimeter =
area =

b.

3cm

3 cm

3cm

c.

5cm

perimeter =
area =

10cm

2cm

6cm

3cm

Challenge

The perimeter of a square is 36cm. What is its area?

☐ cm²

A rectangle has an area of 36cm². Each side is an exact number of cm. What could the perimeter be in cm?

☐ cm

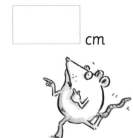

The area of a square is 64cm². What is its perimeter?

☐ cm

Area = 64cm²

Practice

124	93	274	77	131	102

- Which three numbers total 500?
- What is the largest total with 3 numbers?
- Which pair of numbers has a difference of 181?
- What is the smallest total with 3 numbers?

- Total the odd numbers.
- Total the even numbers.

- What would be the cost of a computer and monitor?
- How much would a computer, software and a printer cost?
- How much change would you have from £500 after buying a camera and scanner?
- Jacob has £1000. How much more must he save to buy a computer and a digital camera?
- Lisa saves £25 each month. How many months before she can buy a printer and software?

Challenge

I think of a number.
- If I subtract 19 and divide by 5, the answer is 15.
- What is my number?

I think of a number.
- If I add 99 then multiply by 2, the answer is 800.
- What is my number?

What went into the machine? **in →** +99 → −19 → 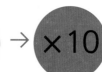 ×10 **out →** 1750

Money problems

Practice

• Total £4.62, £12.40 and £2.76 →

• Total £3.25, 98p and 47p →

• How much change would you have from £10 after spending £2.99 and £3.66? →

• How much change would you have from £20 buying two books costing £7.99 each? →

• Find the cost of each of these.

4 cost £2	→	1 costs
10 cost £3.80	→	1 costs
3 cost £1.26	→	1 costs
1 costs 81p	→	4 cost
1 costs £1.15	→	3 cost

6 cost £7.20	→	1 costs
5 cost £24.75	→	1 costs
8 cost £4.00	→	1 costs
1 costs 93p	→	5 cost
1 costs £1.75	→	4 cost

Challenge

• Ian saves 35p each week. How many weeks does he take to reach £10?

• Astrid saves £1.25 each week. How many weeks does she take to reach £100?

• Sam saves £1.75 each week. How many weeks does she take to reach £50?

• Malcolm saves £2 each week. How many weeks does he take to reach £65?

• Lyn saves 43p each week. How many weeks does she take to reach £58?

• Rob saves £15 each week. How many weeks does he take to save £300?

Divisibility

Look and learn

One number is divisible by another if there is no remainder.

56 is divisible by 8 but not by 9 (56 ÷ 8 = 7)

The **factors** of a number (or numbers something is divisible by) are often put in order or pairs.

Factors of 12 → 1, 2, 3, 4, 6 and 12 in order

→ (1,12)   (2,6)   (3,4) in pairs

Practice

Write true or false for each of these.

375 is divisible by 5	→		83 is divisible by 7	→	
864 is divisible by 2	→		764 is divisible by 4	→	
360 is divisible by 10	→		96 is divisible by 6	→	

Write all the pairs of factors for each number.

28 → [ ]   32 → [ ]   45 → [ ]   81 → [ ]

Challenge

Draw arrows to show all the factors of each number. Write the pairs of factors down.

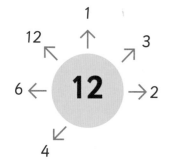

1

12   ↑   3

6 ←   **12**   → 2

4

18   30   90

(1,12) (2,6)
(3,4)

22

Place value: decimals

Look and learn

The decimal point separates units from tenths.

tens	units	•	tenths	hundredths
2	4	•	2	5
twenty	four **point**		two	five

Digits are the numbers 0, 1, 2, 3, 4, 5, 6, 7, 8 and 9.
In a number, each digit has a place value.

$$4 \cdot 73 = 4 + \frac{7}{10} + \frac{3}{100}$$

Practice

Write these using decimal numbers.

six point four five	
nine and two tenths	
twelve and five hundredths	
sixty point zero nine	
nought point nought four	

Write the value of the coloured digit.

72·75	
33·68	
28·25	
35·27	
54·19	

Multiply each number by 10.

6·3	
0·75	
£1·25	
3·5cm	
20·04	

Divide each number by 10.

27	
5	
£9	
2.5m	
5.5	

Challenge

Look at the number machines. Complete each table.

in → **× 100** out →

in	2.3	5.7	0.7	0.08
out				

in → **÷ 100** out →

in	150	132	13	7
out				

Multilplication

Look and learn

There are some useful strategies to learn when multiplying numbers too big to do in your head.

$$26 \times 34 \rightarrow$$

	20	6
30	600	180
4	80	24

```
  600
  180
   80
+  24
  884
```

or

```
   26
 × 34
  780    30 × 26
 +104    4 × 26
  884
```

Practice

Answer these.

```
  28        32
× 27      × 45
```

```
  53        68
× 18      × 55
```

Calculate the areas of each of these rectangles.

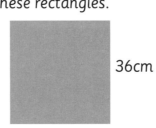
36cm

36cm

Area = _____

12.5 m

1.5 m

Area = _____

• Tickets cost £16 each. What will 24 cost?
_____

• A pack of cheese nibbles weighs 36g. What will 36 bags weigh?
_____

• A driver travels 96km each week. How far will he go in one year?
_____

• There are 12 eggs on a tray. How many eggs on 48 trays?
_____

Challenge

Use these digits:

| 7 | 3 | 4 | 5 |

Use each one only once.

```
  ☐ ☐        ☐ ☐
×   ☐ ☐    ×   ☐ ☐
─────       ─────
```

• Arrange them to make the largest possible answer: _____

• Arrange them to make the smallest possible answer: _____

Division

Look and learn

There are some useful strategies to learn when dividing numbers too big to do in your head.

$$197 \div 6 = \quad 6\overline{)197}$$

```
           32   remainder 5
197 ÷ 6 =  6 ) 197
          -180   30 × 6
          ----
            17
           -12   2 × 6
          ----
             5
```

As a quick estimate:

$$197 \div 6 \approx 200 \div 5$$
$$= 40$$

$\approx$ means approximately

Practice

Answer these.

$4\overline{)756}$ $7\overline{)914}$

$5\overline{)907}$ $8\overline{)645}$

619
444
602
358
696

• Which of these numbers can be divided exactly by 7?

• Which of these numbers has a remainder of 3 when divided by 8?

• Which of these numbers is exactly divisible by 4?

• Which of these numbers has an answer of 74 when divided by 6?

• Which of these numbers has a remainder of 4 when divided by 6?

Challenge

Write the missing digit.

$6\overline{)4\square 8} = 73$

$9\overline{)610} = \square 7 \text{ r7}$

$7\overline{)38\square} = 54 \text{ r2}$

$5\overline{)\square 73} = 54 \text{ r3}$

$4\overline{)\square 58} = 89 \text{ r2}$

$\square\overline{)785} = 98 \text{ r1}$

Fractions and decimals

Look and learn

Fractions can be used to divide quantities.

$$\frac{2}{5} \text{ of } £120$$

$\frac{1}{5}$ = £24, therefore

$\frac{2}{5}$ = £24 × 2 = £48

To reduce a fraction to its smallest, you need to cancel.

$$0.6 = \frac{6}{10}$$

divide by 2 and cancel $\quad \frac{\cancel{6}^3}{\cancel{10}_5}$

$$0.6 = \frac{3}{5}$$

To cancel, divide the top and bottom by the **same** number.

$$\frac{8}{12} \begin{matrix} \div 4 \\ \div 4 \end{matrix} = \frac{2}{3}$$

Practice

Answer these.

$\frac{2}{5}$ of 120m =

$\frac{3}{4}$ of 64km =

$\frac{7}{10}$ of £45 =

$\frac{2}{3}$ of 90ml =

$\frac{4}{5}$ of 675g =

Write these as fractions.

- 0·4 =

- 0·2 =

- 0·75 =

- 0·8 =

- 0·25 =

- 0·35 =

Write <, > or = in the boxes.

$\frac{2}{5}$ ☐ 0·2

$\frac{1}{3}$ ☐ 0·4

$\frac{3}{4}$ ☐ 0·3

$\frac{4}{10}$ ☐ 0·45

$\frac{1}{4}$ ☐ 0·75

Challenge

Write these in order, starting with the smallest.

0.5m $\frac{1}{3}$ m   600cm → ◯ ◯ ◯

0.75kg $\frac{2}{3}$ kg   600g → ◯ ◯ ◯

0.25l $\frac{1}{5}$ ml   280ml → ◯ ◯ ◯

Percentages

Look and learn

% shows a fraction out of 100.

$40\% = \dfrac{40}{100}$

$25\% = \dfrac{25}{100}$

% also means percentage

Common percentages.

- $10\% = \dfrac{10}{100} = \dfrac{1}{10} = 0{\cdot}1$
- $25\% = \dfrac{25}{100} = \dfrac{1}{4} = 0{\cdot}25$
- $50\% = \dfrac{50}{100} = \dfrac{1}{2} = 0{\cdot}5$

- 1% of £1 = 1p
- 10% of £1 = 10p
- 20% of £1 = 20p
- 50% of £1 = 50p

Practice

Write the % shown in colour.

Write these as a % .

$\dfrac{3}{10} =$

$\dfrac{3}{4} =$

$\dfrac{4}{5} =$

$\dfrac{3}{20} =$

$\dfrac{7}{10} =$

Answer these.

- 10% of £2 =
- 50% of £8 =
- 25% of £10 =
- 5% of £3 =
- 20% of £35 =
- 80% of £50 =

Challenge

Abdul made a cake.

400g

CAKE RECIPE

- 35% dried fruit
- 15% butter
- 30% flour
- 10% sugar
- 10% eggs and nuts

Write the weight of each ingredient.

- dried fruit =
- butter =
- flour =
- sugar =
- eggs and nuts =

Data (3)

Practice

The graphs show how two cyclists performed in a race.

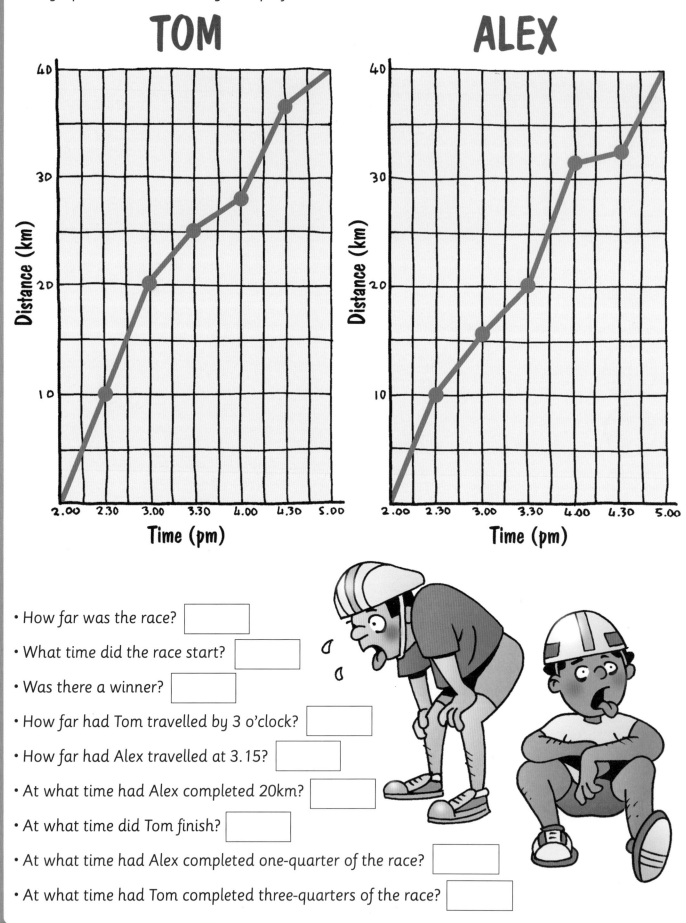

TOM

ALEX

• How far was the race? ☐

• What time did the race start? ☐

• Was there a winner? ☐

• How far had Tom travelled by 3 o'clock? ☐

• How far had Alex travelled at 3.15? ☐

• At what time had Alex completed 20km? ☐

• At what time did Tom finish? ☐

• At what time had Alex completed one-quarter of the race? ☐

• At what time had Tom completed three-quarters of the race? ☐

Shape (3)

Look and learn

90° is a **right** angle.

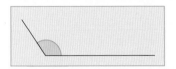

An **obtuse** angle is between 90° and 180°.

An **acute** angle is less than 90°.

A **reflex** angle is more than 180°.

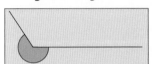

A straight line is 180°.

Practice

Look for obtuse angles inside these shapes. Tick them.

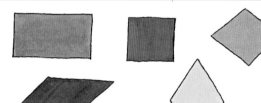

These questions are about the diagonals of shapes:

• Whose diagonals cross at right angles?

• Whose diagonals cut each other in half?

• Whose diagonals are the same length?

Join these angles in order of size. Start with the smallest.

Challenge

Write the size of the missing angles.

A.

140° ?°

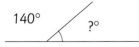

B.

145° ?°

A =

B =

C.

?° 80°

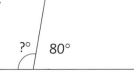

D.

125° ?°

C =

D =

Time

Look and learn

am means → ante meridian, which is in **the morning**.

pm means → post meridian, which is in **the afternoon**.

A new day starts immediately after midnight:

23	59

1 minute before midnight

00	01

1 minute after midnight

12	00

Noon

Practice

Join the matching times.

4.25pm		20:50
3.10am		16:25
8.05am		03:10
8.50pm		04:52
4.52am		08:05

Train timetable

Lindon	06:10	08:00	10:30	13:00
Petersdean	07:06	08:49	11:15	13:49
Neverthorpe	07:35	–	–	14:20
Dincaster	08:07	09:37	12:05	14:50
Wallop	08:33	10:03	12:30	15:05
Dinely	09:35	11:05	13:19	16:15
Glandon	11:09	12:39	14:51	17:55

• What time does the 08:00 Lindon train reach Wallop?

• Which train from Petersdean would you take to be in Glandon by 1.00pm?

• How long does the 06:10 train from Lindon take to reach Glandon?

Challenge

Tick the most appropriate answer.

• To roast a chicken:
  - 10 hours ☐
  - 5 hours ☐
  - 2 hours ☐

• To walk a kilometre:
  - 15 mins ☐
  - 45 mins ☐
  - 75 mins ☐

• To run 100 metres:
  - 20 seconds ☐
  - 2 minutes ☐
  - 20 minutes ☐

• Years in a millennium:
  - 100 ☐
  - 1000 ☐
  - 1 000 000 ☐

• Years in a decade:
  - 10 ☐
  - 100 ☐
  - 1000 ☐

• Years in a century:
  - 10 ☐
  - 100 ☐
  - 1000 ☐

Addition and subtraction (2)

Look and learn

You should know . . .

• 2-digit numbers that total 100:
$26 + 47 + 27$

• Multiples of 50 which total 1000:
$350 + 650$

• Tenths which total 1:
$0{\cdot}7 + 0{\cdot}3$

• Tenths which total 10:

$3{\cdot}5 + 6{\cdot}5$

Practice

a. Work these out.

3854 add 700 = ☐   Decrease 93 by 68 = ☐

1426 subtract 60 = ☐   Total of 573 and 99 = ☐

Increase 190 by 87 = ☐   Taking 99 from 814 = ☐

c. Write the missing numbers.

$0{\cdot}4 +$ ☐ $= 1$ $4{\cdot}2 +$ ☐ $= 10$

☐ $+ 0{\cdot}8 = 1$ ☐ $+ 3{\cdot}9 = 10$

$1 -$ ☐ $= 0{\cdot}9$ $10 -$ ☐ $= 1{\cdot}4$

b. Write the missing numbers.

$36 +$ ☐ $= 100$ ☐ $+ 94 = 100$

$71 +$ ☐ $= 100$ $100 -$ ☐ $= 15$

☐ $+ 23 = 100$ $100 -$ ☐ $= 62$

d. Write the missing numbers.

$250 +$ ☐ $= 1000$ ☐ $+ 850 = 1000$

$450 +$ ☐ $= 1000$ $1000 -$ ☐ $= 150$

☐ $+ 150 = 1000$ $1000 -$ ☐ $= 850$

Challenge

The three corner numbers total the middle number. Write the missing number.

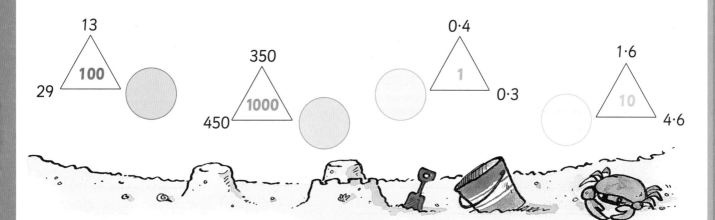

Numbers (2)

Look and learn

Square numbers are when two identical numbers are multiplied together.

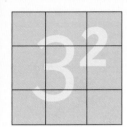

$3 \times 3 = 9$ this is written as → $3^2 = 9$

3 squared = nine

9 is a square number

Practice

a. What is 4 squared? ☐

What is 10 squared? ☐

What is 7 squared? ☐

What is 5 squared? ☐

What is 8 squared? ☐

c.

☐ × ☐ = 81

☐ × ☐ = 9

☐ × ☐ = 100

☐ × ☐ = 64

☐ × ☐ = 36

b.

$9^2 = $ ☐ $7^2 = $ ☐

$6^2 = $ ☐ $2^2 = $ ☐

$3^2 = $ ☐ $12^2 = $ ☐

d.

12 m

Area =

Challenge

Work out the missing lengths.

Area = 81 cm²   ↑   ☐ cm   ↓

Area = 72 cm²   ↑ ☐ cm ↓

 ← 12 cm →